The Huge Rude Duke

Clive Gifford

Illustrated by Katy Taggart

When he was born, the Duke of Bude looked cute.
But by the time he was five, he was a spoilt **rude** brute.

His nanny used to feed him
with all sorts of food.
She fed him on flans,
cornflakes and cakes.

She never told him off for being rude.
And she did not tell him to be nice to others.
The Duke was an only child.
So he never had to share things
with sisters or brothers.

Which of these words can be made into new words by adding the letter e to the end? Write each new word three times.

bag	hug	us	hub	cut	tub	red	cub

♥ 6 ♣ 5 ♦ 4 ♠ 3 ♦ 2 ♣ 1 ♥

1 ♣ 2 ♦ 3 ♠ 4

1. _____ _____ _____

2. _____ _____ _____

3. _____ _____ _____

4. _____ _____ _____

5. _____ _____ _____

4 ♣ 3 ♦ 2 ♠ 1

♥ 1 ♣ 2 ♦ 6 ♠ 4 ♦ 5 ♣ 6 ♥

As a rule, most rude children
learn to be good in the end.
And most grow up
to be super adults
and have lots of friends.

But the Duke of Bude
was not one to follow rules.

By the time he was ten,
he was the rudest in school.

By the time he was twenty,
he was the rudest in Bude.

By the time he was thirty,
he was the rudest man alive!

And not just rude, but **greedy**, too.

Refusing food was something the Duke would never do!

4

This is one of Cook's shopping lists, which the rude Duke tore up in a temper. Can you match the pieces of paper to make up the list?

ten cream

a bottle of

five tins

a shiny

three strawberry

a packet of

of tuna

chocolate flakes

and cream flans

tomato sauce

brass tuba

cakes

"Knickers!" cried the Duke.
It amused him to be rude.

"Bottoms!" roared the
Duke. He was ever so crude.

The smallest thing made
the Duke blow his fuse.
Then he would fume and
throw food around the room.
Sometimes, he would throw
his servants, too.

After he had fumed, the mess had to be cleared up by June.
June was a cleaner, who was smart and cute.
She and her friend, Doug, had a plan to trick the rude Duke.

If you put either **fl** or **cl** at the start of these groups of letters, you can make a word. Write each of the words twice.

ake   _____   _____

ear   _____   _____

at   _____   _____

ush   _____   _____

ean   _____   _____

ose   _____   _____

ea   _____   _____

othes   _____   _____

One day, the Duke was being rude to Cook.
"You ugly old prune!" fumed the Duke.
"I hate bad food."

"This cake has only five choc-flakes.
Feed it to the mules!"

"What can I get you now, Sir?"
said the butler, Mr Rules.

"I want to hear Shane
play his music, you fool!"

"Would your Dukeness prefer my flute or my lute?" asked Shane.

"I would rather be nude than hear your stupid flute or lute.
I want more **volume**, so my new tuba would suit my mood."

Can you match the words to the pictures of musical instruments?

drum

lute

flute

gong

tuba

harp

bell

banjo

Down in the kitchens, the servants had some tea.
Doug the gardener ate some of the cake
with five choc-flakes.

"I wonder how Shane is doing?" said June.
She did not have to wait long –
the answer came soon.
Down the clothes chute flew Shane
with the tuba on his head.
In his hands were his br⁰kᵉn
lute and ruined flute.

"I told the Duke I could not
play the tuba!" cried Shane.
"The Duke blew his fuse,
as I could not play a tune.
And now he is looking for someone
to help him choose a new costume."

Change the second letter in each of these words to make a word found in the story.

 shack   _____

Jane   _____

 ride   _____

late   _____

 thick   _____

moles   _____

11

"I will go," said June. "We have a super plan to dupe the Duke."

"I have grown a Crazy Maze out of spruce trees," said Doug. "And we need you, Cook, to fill it with food."

Whilst Cook cooked, June chose a new costume for the Duke.

Five hours later, June saluted the Duke in his new suit. "Excuse me, Duke, but you look super in blue wool. And I have some news that might amuse you. Your amazing Crazy Maze is ready and it is full of lovely food."

Some words have a silent letter, such as the letter g in sign and the letter n at the end of autumn. Say each word and circle the silent letter.

k n i c k e r s

g h o s t

w r i t e

D o u g

k n e e

t w o

June led the rude Duke outside to the **Crazy Maze**.

"You could make a trail in the maze with the wool in your costume. Then, once full of food, you can find your way out soon."

As the Duke waddled into the maze, June rushed inside the house.

"Oh, June," said the cook. "Have we really duped the Duke?"

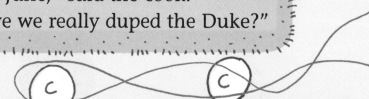

Mr Rules coughed and everyone went quiet. "I hope, June, you have not duped the Duke of Bude!" smiled Mr Rules.

14

"He will be in the maze for days, so we will have time for a super party!"

 Each of these words is missing the letter U. Can you work out where the letter should go and write out each word?

r d e _____

s p e r _____

t b e _____

s a l t e _____

m l e _____

b r t e _____

e x c s e _____

c o m p t e r _____

Back in the Crazy Maze, the Duke was in a daze.
After every turn in the maze, there was so much food to consume.

"Aha, a prune stew, flans and cakes with more than five choc-flakes!"
The rude Duke ate all the food and was getting **huge**.

"Not bad for a snack," he said, leaving his trail of blue wool.

A few hours later, the rude Duke was ever so huge.
"I must get back, it will be dinner time soon," said the Duke.

He used the wool to find his way to the maze gates.
But was so big he could not fit through.
Now he would be late!

Trace a route round each maze to find the hidden words. No doubling back, now! Then write each word in the space below.

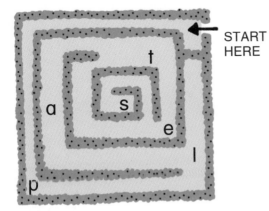

START HERE

t
a
s
e
l
p

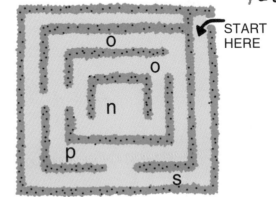

START HERE

o
o
n
p
s

_____

_____

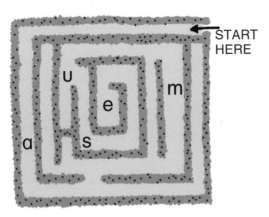

START HERE

u
m
e
a
s

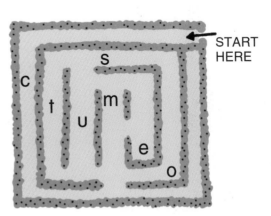

START HERE

s
c
t
m
u
e
o

_____

_____

"Just a fluke," said the rude Duke. "I will try again."
He tried, but was too huge to get through.

"**KNICKERS!**" he shouted rudely
at Cook, Shane, Doug and June.

"Well, knickers to you too, Duke!"
laughed Cook.

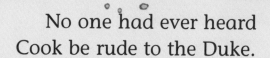

No one had ever heard
Cook be rude to the Duke.

"Get me out, you crazy, lazy prunes,
you stupid mules," the Duke fumed.

"Does Sir think the Duke of Bude
should be seen like that?" said Mr Rules.

"Seen like what?" said the Duke.
He was not amused!

All the words below mean either big or small. Can you write each one in the right list?

large   massive   tiny   petite   huge   little
giant   miniature   microscopic   enormous

big

_____

_____

_____

_____

_____

small

_____

_____

_____

_____

_____

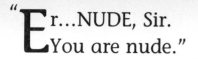
"**E**r...NUDE, Sir. You are nude."

The Duke looked down and saw just a trail of blue wool.
The huge, rude Duke of Bude was now nude!
His face went a bright cherry red with rage.

"We could call a truce, if you stop being rude..." smiled Doug. "We might help you out in a day or two!"

The Duke learned his lesson and agreed to end the feud. And now he is no longer known as the rude Duke of Bude.

If you know the story of The Huge Rude Duke, then try to answer the questions below.

1. How old was the Duke by the time he was the rudest man in Bude?

_____

2. What job did June do at the Duke's house?

_____

3. The Duke refused to eat a cake. How many flakes did it have?

_____

4. What was the name of the Duke's butler?

_____

5. The Duke's musician carried two musical instruments with him. What were they?

_____

6. Who flew down the clothes chute with a tuba on his head?

_____

Answers

Page 3

1. hug ➜ huge
2. us ➜ use
3. cut ➜ cute
4. tub ➜ tube
5. cub ➜ cube

Page 5

ten cream cakes
a bottle of tomato sauce
five tins of tuna
a shiny brass tuba
three strawberry and cream flans
a packet of chocolate flakes

Page 7

flake
clear
flat
flush
clean
close
flea
clothes

Page 9

drum

lute

flute

gong

tuba

harp

bell

banjo

Page 11

shack ➜ snack

Jane ➜ June

ride ➜ rude

late ➜ lute

thick ➜ trick

moles ➜ mules

Page 13

(k)n i c k e r s

D (o) u g

(w) r i t e

(k) n e e

g (h) o s t

t (w) o

Page 15

rude

super

tube

salute

mule

brute

cxcuse

computer

Page 17

plates

spoon

amuse

costume

Page 19

big: large, massive, huge, giant, enormous

small: tiny, petite, little, miniature, microscopic

Page 21

1. twenty
2. a cleaner
3. five
4. Mr Rules
5. a flute and a lute
6. Shane

Published 2004

10 9 8 7 6 5 4 3 2

Letts Educational, The Chiswick Centre,
414 Chiswick High Road, London W4 5TF
Tel 020 8996 3333 Fax 020 8996 8390
Email mail@lettsed.co.uk
www.letts-education.com

Book Concept, Development and Series Editor:
Helen Jacobs, Publishing Director
Author: Clive Gifford
Book Design: 2idesign Ltd, Cambridge
Illustrations: Katy Taggart, The Bright Agency

Letts Educational Limited is a division of Granada Learning.
Part of Granada plc.

British Library Cataloguing in Publication Data

A CIP record for this book is available from the British Library.

ISBN 1 84315 452 8

Printed in Italy

Colour reproduction by PDQ Digital Media Limited, Bungay, Suffolk